*The story of the plague at Eyam*

Margaret McAllister

Illustrated by Alice Englander

OXFORD
UNIVERSITY PRESS

OXFORD
UNIVERSITY PRESS

Great Clarendon Street, Oxford OX2 6DP

Oxford University Press is a department of the University of Oxford.
It furthers the University's objective of excellence in research, scholarship,
and education by publishing worldwide in

Oxford New York

Auckland Cape Town Dar es Salaam Hong Kong Karachi
Kuala Lumpur Madrid Melbourne Mexico City Nairobi
New Delhi Shanghai Taipei Toronto

With offices in

Argentina Austria Brazil Chile Czech Republic France Greece
Guatemala Hungary Italy Japan Poland Portugal Singapore
South Korea Switzerland Thailand Turkey Ukraine Vietnam



First published 2003



British Library Cataloguing in Publication Data

Data available

ISBN: 978-0-19-919659-3

15 17 19 20 18 16 14

Mixed Pack (1 of 6 different titles): ISBN: 978-0-19-919662-3
Class Pack (6 copies of 6 titles): ISBN: 978-0-19-919661-6

Illustrated by Alice Englander

**Acknowledgements**
p1 Eyam P.C.C./Heritage House Group Ltd; p4 Bettmann/
Corbis UK Ltd.; p4/5 Corel; p5 John Clifford; p13 John Clifford;
p20 Garden Picture Library; p71 Taxi/Getty Images; p76 Mary
Evans Picture Library; p78 Corbis UK Ltd.; p78 Corel; p79 (top)
Eyam P.C.C./Heritage House Group Ltd; p79 (bottom) George
D. Lepp/Corbis UK Ltd.

With thanks from the author to the following:
Eyam Museum staff; Nicola Wright; Dr. Claire Parsons;
Tony Buglass; Francine Clifford; John Clifford

Printed in Malaysia by
MunSang Printers Sdn Bhd

Paper used in the production of this book is a natural,
recyclable product made from wood grown in sustainable forests.
The manufacturing process conforms to the environmental
regulations of the country of origin.

# Contents

# Introduction

**London**. In 1665, the **plague** brought death and misery.

There was headache, weakness and fever. Then came the sore, red swellings, which grew harder and angrier until they burst and spread the infection further.

There was thirst, pain and delirium. Skin blackened under the surface. Londoners learned to fear coughs and sneezes, to fear crowds, to fear each other. Few who caught it recovered.

In London's cramped streets in summer, plague spread like fire. When one member of a family fell ill, the rest would follow. It destroyed, and could not be stopped.

**Eyam** (pronounced "eeam"). It was a happy, prosperous village deep in the beautiful countryside of Derbyshire, surrounded by hills and moors.

What could the nightmare of the London plague have to do with little Eyam?

*Eyam church today*

*(left) Street scene during the London plague, from 1665. Distraught pedestrians are out in the street. The town crier is calling out "Bring out your dead". The dead are placed in a cart to be driven away*

# CHAPTER 1

# July

"Do you feel well? Do you hurt anywhere? Stand still."

It was the same first thing every morning. Lizzie lined up the younger children, Joan, Robin, and Christopher, in order of age while they wriggled and fidgeted. She felt their foreheads in case they were hot and checked under their arms for lumps.

Sarah was twelve, red-haired, and freckled. She checked herself before lacing up her **bodice**. She had her dignity to think of. Besides, she had already looked for signs of plague under her arms this morning. Twice. Robin squirmed as Lizzie anxiously peered under one of his arms, then the other, before pulling his shirt back into place with a sigh of relief. She took off her coarse apron and smoothed her gown.

"Let's have you all ready for church, then," she said.

"We can't go to church," said Robin.

"Church meeting, Cucklett Delph," snapped Lizzie. "Don't stand close to anyone. If the wind blows..."

"...turn your faces away!" chanted Robin and Christopher together, and giggled until Lizzie slapped Robin for cheek.

"Why just me, and not Christopher?" demanded Robin.

"Because you're big enough to know better," said Lizzie.

Sarah knelt beside Robin. His chubby, new puppy, Penn, was licking his smacked hand. “Lizzie’s worried,” said Sarah. “That’s why she gets cross these days.”

It was only half true. Lizzie had always found plenty to be cross about. With mother dead and four younger brothers and sisters to look after, maybe she had to be bossy, but she wasn’t as bad as this before the plague.

Before the plague. Had there ever been such a time? Sarah sometimes thought she had dreamed it. On spring days, they used to meet their friends at the market in Bakewell, share their news, eat gingerbread, and giggle about who was courting. Before the plague, women chatted in doorways, and children played together in the street. It all seemed far, far away, in another world.

Now, it felt as if they had always lived with plague, never leaving the village, always wondering who would be next. Every night when Sarah went to bed, she thanked God for one more day. Every morning, she prayed for another. Let me live today, please God. Not plague. Please not today.

"Can I take Penn to church?" said Robin, hugging the puppy. "Please, Lizzie?"

"Certainly not!" said Lizzie. "We don't take dogs to church. And don't go saying 'it's Cucklett Delph'. It may only be a hill, but it's all the church we've got, now."

The church had been closed since June, because it was dangerous for people to be together in a closed space. There were no more burials in the churchyard, either. The dead were buried quickly in the hills or the fields, without much of a funeral. The vicar had more than enough to do caring for the dying and the orphans, without burying the dead – and there were many dead, since the plague came.

Mr Viccars, the tailor, had been first. He had ordered cloth from London. Everyone knew that plague was raging there, but nobody had guessed that it could be carried in a parcel of cloth. That had never occurred

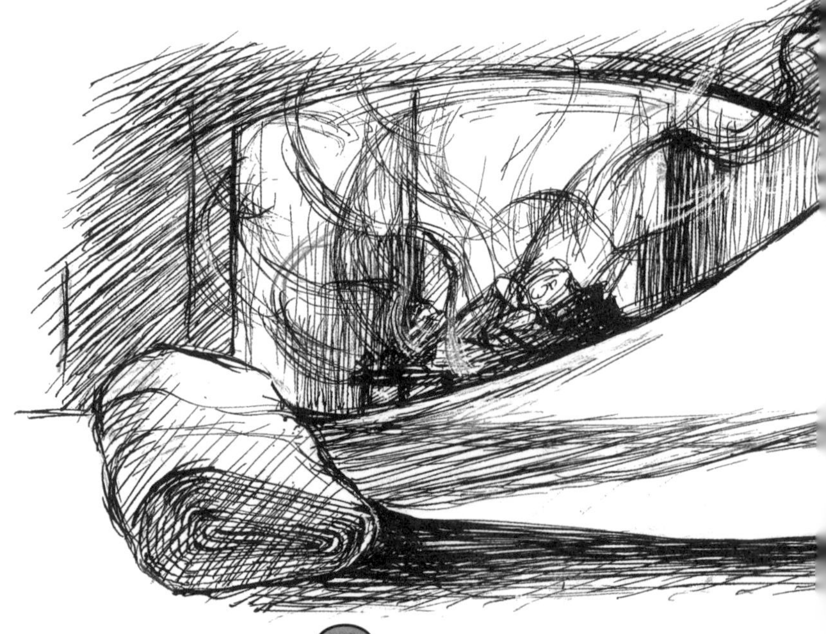

to anyone. Certainly not to Mr Viccars, who unwrapped the cloth, aired it by the fire, and was dead a week later. There were more plague deaths in September and during the winter.

By May it seemed to be over – but the warm June weather brought plague lashing back through the village, destroying family after family. Mr Mompesson the vicar and Mr Stanley, who had been vicar before him, talked earnestly together in the vicarage. Then they called the people together.

CHAPTER

2

# Cucklett Delph

By the time Mr Mompesson called that meeting, some families had already left the village. Mr and Mrs Mompesson had sent their two little children away. But there must be no more. Plague was killing its way through Eyam, and there was little they could do about that. But the people of Eyam could do one thing. They could stop it from spreading throughout Derbyshire and beyond.

*The Boundary Stone is still there today*

Together, they made their decision. Until the plague was over, nobody would leave Eyam. Nobody could come in and risk taking plague away with them.

"But we will starve!" grumbled somebody; but Mr Mompesson and Mr Stanley had thought of that. Supplies of food and anything they needed could be brought to the **Boundary Stone** on the edge of the village, or to the well near it. Money to pay would be left in running water or in vinegar, to cleanse it.

Eyam would keep its fate to itself. Cut off from the world, the village would wait until the plague had burnt itself out.

In the meantime, those who were alive must go on with the business of staying alive. There was work, food, keeping house, minding the children, and Sunday worship to keep them busy. It was better to be occupied.

Sarah's whole house smelt of stale smoke and vinegar. Lizzie sprinkled vinegar about in the hope that it would keep plague away, and she made Father smoke tobacco for the same reason. Bunches of herbs hung at every window. They might work. Anything was worth trying.

"Will there be any parcels at the Boundary Stone, today?" said Christopher.

"I should think not, not on a Sunday!" said Lizzie.

Their Father appeared in the Sunday clothes that looked as if they belonged to someone else, and they set off down the street.

Children no longer played together. Lizzie took Father's arm to show off her position as the eldest daughter and mistress of the house. Sarah kept a firm hold on Christopher's hand, knowing that in time he would stop wriggling and pulling, and walk quietly.

Robin, who was seven, and Joan, who was nine, were dark and sturdily built. They walked in front of Sarah, teasing, sulking, giggling and squabbling until Joan pushed Robin and he pushed her back. She tripped, grabbing at Lizzie's gown to steady herself. Lizzie turned sharply.

"Walk like a decent person, Joan!" she ordered, and glared at Sarah. "Keep them in order, can't you?"

Sarah pulled a face at Lizzie's back. If Lizzie expects me to look after the children, she should stop treating me as a child myself. Telling me off in the street like that!

Up at Cucklett Delph, the hillside opened into a sweeping arc as if it held out its arms to them.

While the church was closed this was where the village met for worship, but they stood back from each other. Families stayed in their own separate huddles. Married daughters nodded and waved to their parents, but stayed well away and held their children close to them. Small children who tried to run to their friends were held back. Christopher looked wistfully at his friends and Sarah ached for them all. They should be running about and playing not huddled close to their families. And, week by week, there were fewer little children.

Robin sneezed. Sarah jumped. Please, God, don't let Robin die. It had become a habit to think these prayers, she did it when anyone in the family coughed or complained of feeling poorly.

"I couldn't help it," said Robin, as Lizzie glared at him. "Christopher tickled my nose with a grass."

"Then, don't, Christopher!" snapped Lizzie. Christopher's eyes filled with tears, and Sarah hugged him.

They were all suffering from Lizzie's strained nerves. Sarah brushed away the hair blowing into her eyes and looked to see who else was there. Mr Mompesson stood high on the rock overlooking them all. His pretty, young wife looked pale and tired, and she coughed, but Mrs Mompesson always coughed.

Old Mr and Mrs Unwin waved to her. Mr Unwin had a rough, gruff manner but he was kind-hearted, and Mrs Unwin always gave the children an apple or pennies when they ran errands for her. She had the most beautiful silver candlesticks, and Sarah loved to polish them. Robin's dog had been a present from the Unwins, when their terrier had puppies. As soon as the bright-eyed, plump, little pup was brought home she had rolled in the clump of **pennyroyal** growing at the front door. So Robin had called her 'Pennyroyal'. Pennyroyal, then Pennyro, Penny, Penn. It couldn't get shorter.

Mother had planted the pennyroyal, when Christopher was a baby.

*Pennyroyal. The Latin name is Mentha Pulegium*

She was proud of keeping a clean house, and said that pennyroyal kept fleas away. It seemed to work, because Penn never got fleas.

Sarah watched butterflies dancing in the air and ladybirds crawling over grass stalks. Plague was nothing to them. They weren't trapped in Eyam village. When Mr Mompesson began the prayers, she listened. There was such a long list of people who were ill.

Sarah's friend James wasn't on that list. He was at the end of the next, long list. The list of the dead.

James had been more alive than anyone. He never walked anywhere, only ran. Never opened a gate if he could jump over it, couldn't see a pebble without kicking it down the street. Now he was dead, and Marshall Howe the gravedigger had dragged him away in a sheet.

Sometimes, she felt it would be better not to care about anyone. Not if they're about to die.

"It smells nice up here," said Joan as they went home.

"What?" said Lizzie. A sweet smell in the nostrils was an early sign of plague.

"It's only the scent of clover," said Father calmly.

They saw Marshall Howe as they walked back into the village. He hadn't been to worship. With his hunched, heavy tread, his scowling face and his muddy boots, he was pulling something wrapped in a stained sheet. Lizzie hustled the children well out of the way.

"Turn your faces away," she ordered. Sarah pressed Christopher's face against her skirt.

"I hate Marshall Howe," whispered Robin fiercely.

"Mr Mompesson says we mustn't hate," said Lizzie, but nobody liked Marshall Howe. He had caught plague himself, and recovered. Not many did. Now, because he could not catch it again, he was the one who went without fear into plague houses to drag away the dead. Then, to pay for his services, he would go back to the house and help himself to whatever he wanted – the best plates, furnishings or silver, if the family had any. Nobody dared argue with him. He left his burden lying in the street and walked towards them.

"Stop there, Howe!" called Father.

Marshall Howe stopped. "You want to sell me your pup?" he called.

"What, you mean Robin's pup?" said Father, "He's keeping it."

Howe shrugged. "Suit yourself, if you don't want good money," he said, but Robin was already running home to Penn. Marshall Howe had tried more than once to buy the pup. He had said she would turn out badly and offered to take her off their hands, but Robin knew better. Penn was a good rat-catcher, like her mother, and that's why Marshall Howe wanted her.

"I wish we could go to Bakewell market tomorrow," sighed Joan.

"We will, love, when the plague's over," said Father, but they had been saying this all summer. It seemed as if it would go on forever. No going to market. No going outside this tight little village with the fear of death around at every corner.

"Lizzie! Lizzie!" Robin's voice rose, loud and urgent as he ran towards them. "Penn's gone!"

# CHAPTER 3
# Threat

"Marshall Howe's stolen her!" sobbed Robin, and went on sobbing with fury until Sarah found the rope Penn had been tied up with in the yard. It was dog-chewed and soggy.

"Nobody's stolen her," said Father. "She's run off."

"She can't have gone far," said Sarah. "Go and call her, Robin."

They heard him in the yard, desperately calling her name. When he came indoors, he was redder than ever.

"She's nowhere near," he said. "I'm going to look for her."

"Dogs have to look after themselves," said Lizzie firmly. She, too, was pink, but she would not have the small windows opened in case the plague blew in.

"Penn's only a puppy!" wailed Robin. "She'll get lost!"

"She'll come home when she's hungry," said Father.

After dinner, when the pots were scoured and put away and the scraps of food cleared up to give to Penn, the dog was still missing. What was far worse, so was Robin. Fear of where he could be and what could happen to him made Sarah turn hot and cold.

"Sarah!" Lizzie banged her fist on the table. "Can't you look after them? Can't you even count them? What use are you?"

"Now, our Lizzie, that's hard on her," said Father, but Sarah didn't wait to hear more.

"I'll look after him, then!" Banging the door, she ran from the house.

She searched the empty street. At the end of a row of houses where there was plague she stood and looked, covering her mouth, but she went no further. She was glad she didn't have to go down there. She could see a rat in the corner of a wall, washing its whiskers. No Robin. She ran up to Cucklett Delph and climbed to the rock where Mr Mompesson had preached. There were cliffs to fall from, streams to tumble into – wasn't plague alone enough to worry about?

Far away something moved, disappeared behind a rock, and appeared again. It was Penn and, chasing after her, was Robin. Penn saw him, whisked about, and went on running.

"Robin!" screamed Sarah, but Robin took no notice. Sarah gathered up her grey gown and scrambled uphill. There was no point in chasing the puppy, who thought it was all a game and would only run further. Instead, Sarah ran at Robin and finally caught him round the middle while he kicked and thrashed. Finally he stopped struggling, as she knew he would, and cried in her arms.

"She'll go – she'll go – out of the village," he gasped, between sobs. Then she won't be allowed back."

"She certainly will, if you keep chasing her," said Sarah. She wasn't sure if the isolation of the village applied to dogs as well as people. Penn might carry plague on her coat or her paws. "And if you run out of the village following her, what then? You could take plague with you and everybody could get it."

"I'm sick of hearing about plague," said Robin sulkily, and sat down. Presently Penn came and stood at a distance, panting and wondering why the game had stopped.

"She'll follow us," said Sarah. They set out for home with Penn pattering after them. "We must take more care to keep her in, Robin. Find her a leash or a bit of rope that she can't bite through. And a collar."

The smell of food hurried Penn home, and she scampered to the cottage ahead of them. Robin suddenly stopped chattering and stood still, with clenched fists.

Marshall Howe was swaggering towards them with his spade over his shoulder. Sarah turned her face away, but she heard his voice.

"Heard the news?" he called, and she could hear the laughter in that voice. "Plague's worse than ever in London. They're killing all the cats and dogs so they can't spread the plague! And it's started here! Unwin's dog's dead!"

His hoarse laughter followed them home. Robin wrapped his arms round Penn and was still pressing his face into her coat when they got home.

Lizzie pounced. “What do you think you were doing, running off like that? Haven’t we got enough to worry about without you? Do you think we have all day to look for you?” She stopped to breathe, then added, “and that dog stinks of pennyroyal. She’s been rolling in it again.”

“Mr Unwin’s dog’s dead,” cried Robin.

“Everyone knows that,” snapped Lizzie. “Mr Unwin says she had a bad heart. She had a fit and died.”

“But...” began Robin.

“Nothing to do with plague, if that’s what you want to know,” said Lizzie firmly. “Go and wash yourself.”

“Is it true, what Marshall Howe said?” Sarah asked her father, when Robin was out of the way. “Are they really killing cats and dogs in London?”

“How would he know?” said her father. News only reached Eyam if it was shouted across the brook. “Could be right.”

“They won’t do that here, will they?” she said.

He shrugged. "If we're going to catch plague, we will. Killing cats and dogs won't help. But there's folks that would do it, all the same."

Sarah wondered afterwards if Robin had heard any of this. Maybe he had. The next morning, he wasn't there. Neither was Penn.

CHAPTER

4

# leave My Brother Alone!

It was Monday, and that was the hardest day, because Bakewell market was on a Monday. It was weeks since Sarah last went to Bakewell, and she yearned for it. In summer, the colour and brightness of the market made a treat to look forward to.

Today, Eyam folk laboured up the hill to leave money at the well, or at the Boundary Stone. This was where deliveries of food were left, outside the village with its dangers. Sometimes, the Earl's men left supplies and the Earl took no payment for it. The people of Bubnell gave them bread, too, for nothing.

Sarah did not wait to be scolded by Lizzie. She left Christopher with Joan and ran outside to find Robin.

"Have you seen our Robin?" called Sarah, over and over, and at last an old woman pointed up the hill.

"He'll come to no harm," she said. "He's got his dog with him, on a rope."

So Robin hadn't been hunting for Penn, this time. He'd gone on purpose. Sweat made Sarah's coarse gown hot and itchy as she scrambled uphill and at last, coming over a rise, she saw them. Robin, dishevelled and grubby, stood with his back to her, clutching Penn's rope lead in both hands. Opposite him, standing at a distance, was a big, tousle-haired man.

CHAPTER 4

Sarah recognised him. A stone shelter was behind him. Robin looked very small, Penn looked even smaller, and the man looked enormous.

"I didn't come up here so you and the plague could come visiting," he was saying. "Come any nearer and you'll be near enough to hit."

"Leave my brother alone!" shouted Sarah, and added politely, "please, Mr Merrill. He doesn't mean any harm."

Andrew Merrill had been living up here for weeks. He had taken a few belongings and a tame cockerel and gone away to camp in the hills, saying that he'd leave everyone alone and the plague could leave him alone, thank you.

"I came looking for you, Mr Merrill," said Robin. "I'm going to live on the hills, too."

"You're not stopping near me," grunted Merrill. "There's plenty of hill. Gets cold at nights, mind."

"He's not stopping at all," said Sarah quickly. "He's coming home with me."

"I'm not," said Robin, simply. "Marshall Howe says they're going to kill the dogs. They're not getting Penn."

"Marshall Howe?" said Merrill. "He'll say anything but his prayers. Go home to your Lizzie. You'll be wanted."

"I'm not going," said Robin. "They won't get my dog. There's caves at Cucklett Delph, and there's woods up here. I'm going to live outside, with my dog."

"And what will you eat, and what will you drink, and how will you keep warm at night?" demanded Sarah. Penn snapped at a butterfly as it flittered past her.

Robin paused. "I'll get food from home," he said. He turned to her at last with pleading eyes. "You'll ask our Lizzie for me, won't you?"

"And what's Lizzie going to say about that?" she demanded. Even the thought of it frightened her.

"You can tell your Lizzie," said Merrill, "that the little lad will be safer up here in the hills than he is in that plague prison down there. You tell her that. He can live anywhere, so long as he keeps away from me."

If Andrew Merrill said Robin would be safe, it was probably true. After all, he was living outside himself. Sarah went with Robin to have a look at a shallow cave he had found in the hillside. It wasn't luxury, but it would give shelter and the nights had been warm.

"You can't stay up here alone," she said.

"I'll have Penn," said Robin, but Sarah knew that somebody had to stay with him. It might as well be her. They could bring blankets from home to keep out the draughts. Robin would soon get tired of it.

"I haven't checked you today," she said, suddenly. She looked to see if there were swellings, while he glared indignantly at her. So far, so good. The thought of living out of doors wasn't good, but the idea of Robin with plague was far worse.

"Now wait here," she said. "If anyone comes up, keep away. And don't let Penn run off. You don't know what might happen to her if she does."

And that will keep him quiet, she thought, as she turned for home. Far away on the hill, a man was digging. Knowing what that meant, Sarah turned her face away.

Joan and Christopher were playing in the shade of the house. Joan, red and glowing with the heat, was giving Christopher rides on her back. She seemed to be loving her new role as Christopher's best sister.

"Where's Lizzie?" called Sarah.

"In the house, I suppose," called Joan, and went on playing.

The house felt suddenly cool after the sunshine. There was a smell of rosemary, mint and pennyroyal. Lizzie must have just put fresh herbs at the windows. Then Sarah heard something from the upstairs room where they slept.

It was something between a sob and a whimper. Sarah followed the sound upstairs and gently pushed open the door.

CHAPTER

5

# Lizzie

Something that looked like a discarded gown was flung across the bed and trailed on the floor. It was Lizzie, lying face down, sobbing into the blankets.

"Lizzie!" said Sarah. Lizzie jerked with surprise and sat up, gulping. Her face was blotchy with tears.

It's come to us, thought Sarah. We haven't escaped. And though she had lived for months in the fear of plague, she felt a new fear, now it was here. This was gripping terror that tightened her stomach and weakened her legs. It made her sweat and turn cold at the same time.

She was ashamed of herself for stepping back, but she couldn't help it. "Lizzie," she said, "are you sick?"

Lizzie shook her head. “No, I’m not,” she said crossly. She dried her eyes on her apron. “Of course I’m not! None of us are! I keep the children away from everyone. I make Father smoke his tobacco, I put fresh herbs up every day, I’m forever scouring this house with vinegar, I get down and pray, all so we won’t get plague!” Crying again, she pressed her face into her apron.

Sarah had become wary of touching anyone if she could help it. What if Lizzie did have plague? But...

"If she has it, I've got it too," she thought, and with a deep breath and an effort, she took Lizzie in her arms.

"It's been so hard," said Lizzie, tearfully. "Ever since mother died I've tried to do everything the way she taught me. I've kept you all fed and clean and decent, haven't I? I've taught the little ones their manners. I'm always mending their clothes. I do my best. But if the dinner's burned or the little ones catch cold it has to be my fault."

"But you do so well!" insisted Sarah. It pained her to realise that she had never said it before. They all took Lizzie for granted. No wonder she was always cross.

"If Christopher gets scruffy or our Robin answers back, I think everyone's looking at us and saying – 'that Lizzie can't look after her family'. It's always been like that. But since the plague, it's up to me more than ever to keep you all safe."

"But you have kept us safe!" said Sarah.

"So far," she said. "But the Talbot girls are dead. Marshall Howe was digging graves again today. If any of you die, it'll be my fault. What am I to do?"

Sarah held her and rocked her.

"There's not a woman in Eyam keeps her family better than you," she said. "It won't be your fault if we catch – anything. And we won't."

Lizzie rubbed the apron over her face. "And you're going to stop the plague, I suppose, like Moses holding back the Red Sea. Where's Robin?"

Sarah told her about Robin and his plans, and Andrew Merrill. She expected Lizzie to order Robin home at once, but Lizzie seemed too exhausted to argue.

"Maybe Mr Merrill's right," she said. "Maybe it's safer on the hill. At least he won't be trapped in this place."

"And you'll just have Father, Joan and Christopher to look after," said Sarah. "That should be easier. Robin and I can go to the Boundary Stone, if you want anything. If he gets ill, I'll tell you."

"And if anyone here gets ill, I'll warn you," said Lizzie. She spoke in a flat, sad voice, as if the plague had defeated her. "Do you think we'll see this summer out?"

"We'll see this week out," said Sarah. "That'll do. One day, we'll go to market again. I want ribbons for my bonnet." But the important thing was not buying the ribbons. It was the freedom to go to the market and choose them.

"Gloves," said Lizzie. "For Sundays." And they talked of all the things they would do when – not if – the plague was over. At last, Sarah went up the hill with all she thought that she and Robin might need – food, small ale, blankets and some of those herbs, just in case.

Robin loved living out of doors. He missed Christopher, but the freedom to run wild with Penn made up for it. Sarah made him keep Penn on the end of a rope, so she couldn't run beyond the boundary. He climbed trees, tunnelled through bushes, and collected wood to make a fire when the evening grew cold.

There were trips to and from the Boundary Stone where friends from other villages could be seen at a distance, but not spoken to. At nights, cuddled together for warmth, they watched the late glow of the fire and listened for owls and foxes. On fine nights, they lay on their backs and looked at the stars. Sometimes, lying on the hard ground or prickly bracken, Sarah thought wistfully of her bed at home – but at least here she didn't have to share with Joan wriggling and Lizzie talking in her sleep.

She and Lizzie exchanged news. The family stayed well, but not everyone else did. It was never a question of whether anyone else had plague. The question was – who is it this time?

"It's Mr and Mrs Unwin," Lizzie told her, one hot afternoon. "They say Mrs Unwin might come through, but Mr Unwin won't. Mind, don't go near them. There's plenty of folks who are looking after the sick, and taking their chances."

Like Mr and Mrs Mompesson, thought Sarah as she trudged miserably back up the hill. At least, if those two were going to catch it, they would have caught it by now. Mrs Mompesson was so beautiful, and so kind, she mustn't catch plague. Sarah turned and looked down at the village. It had always been home. Now, it was a plague pit.

CHAPTER

# Crisis

The weather grew oppressively hot. There would be thunderstorms. They couldn't stay on the hill. Sarah would have to persuade Robin to go home.

Mr Unwin was said to be near death. Mrs Unwin had recovered, but she was still very frail.

Sarah slept lightly, and woke early with a headache. "It's only an ordinary headache," she thought, and slept again, but it grew worse. She sat up, feeling a little sick. When she stood, she was dizzy.

She felt under her arms. No swellings, but maybe it was too early for that. So she need not worry any more whether she would become ill. It had happened.

She walked from the cave and looked

down from the hill. The world was so beautiful, and she was just beginning to notice it. She and Lizzie were friends at last, since Lizzie had cried in her arms. Then she thought of Robin and her eyes filled, because if she had plague, he probably had it, too.

If she sent him home to Lizzie, he'd give it to all of them. But there was nobody else to look after him. Plague had won.

At least she could make Robin happy for as long as possible. She greeted him with a smile when he woke up, and made sure he had something to eat, though she herself had no appetite. The pain in her head was so strong, it was hard to think of anything else. She hoped it would be over quickly.

In the afternoon, she took Robin and Penn and walked down to the village trying to work out what to say. I'm sorry, Lizzie, I've got plague. Look after Robin. She longed for home but it might be better to go and die on the hill, away from the others.

Penn suddenly jerked free from Robin and tore away down the hill. At the back of a cottage she pounced on something and gave it a furious shaking. Then she trotted proudly back to them, her tail wagging, carrying something in her mouth.

Sarah looked away. She felt ill enough without Penn bringing her a rat. Penn dropped it at her feet.

"Don't touch it, Robin," said Sarah.

Joan and Christopher were playing outside, as usual. Shading her eyes against the sun, Sarah called to them.

"Fetch Lizzie," she said. "And don't come close."

"I'll get her!" Joan's clear voice hammered in the ring of pain in Sarah's head. "Sarah, did you know about Mr Unwin? Marshall Howe's digging his grave! Mrs Unwin doesn't want him in the house, but he's gone anyway!"

In Sarah's spinning head, something became very clear. There was nothing now to stop Marshall Howe from taking the candlesticks.

"Stay there," she said to Robin. She stood up slowly, and thought for a moment she would faint or be sick. With her head pounding, she walked towards the Unwin's house.

Before she reached it, she could hear the thudding. Thump, thump, thump. It banged in her aching head. It was the sound of something heavy in a sheet, being dragged and bumped down the stairs.

Sarah sat down unsteadily and pressed fingertips to her aching head. Mr Unwin was dead. Marshall Howe would certainly take those candlesticks. She imagined Mrs Unwin fretting helplessly in bed while Marshall Howe stuffed her precious candlesticks into his **jerkin**.

She knew she should not sit on the ground in the middle of the street. Lizzie wouldn't approve. But if she didn't sit down she would fall, so she sat in the street outside the Unwin's house and hugged her knees tightly as the door opened.

Marshall Howe came out, dragging a sheet which was wrapped round the body of Mr Unwin in his nightgown. It was shameful, to be pulled along in a nightgown, in the street! She looked away.

"WHAT ARE YOU DOING? GET ME A DRINK, FOR THE LOVE OF GOD!"

Mr Unwin's voice! Sarah jerked with terror.

"Get me a drink!" rasped the voice again, and she stared in horror at the dead man's open eyes. Something between a scream and a bellow came from Marshall Howe as he dropped the sheet.

But Mr Unwin was not dead. Those eyes were alive, the colour had come back into his face, and he was roaring curses at the figure of Marshall Howe as he ran in terror down

the street. Sarah stumbled past Mr Unwin and into the house of plague, for she couldn't catch it if she had it already. She poured ale into a tankard and took it outside where bystanders watched, keeping their distance from Mr Unwin and from each other.

"Here's your drink, Mr Unwin," she said. Her hands were shaking badly, and she tried not to spill.

"Send for Mr Mompesson," urged somebody. "And get Unwin back indoors until he makes up his mind if he's living or dying."

Sarah took the tankard back. In the little parlour, something was not quite right. She looked again.

The candlesticks were gone.

CHAPTER

7

# The Candlesticks

With her head throbbing, Sarah followed the first idea that came to her. She walked unsteadily to Marshall Howe's house and stood at the open door.

Marshall Howe sat at the table, white-faced, pouring out strong liquor and lifting the cup in two shaking hands. He gulped down the drink, and poured another. Mrs Unwin's candlesticks lay on the table.

Sarah steadied herself against the doorpost. When Marshall Howe saw her his mouth fell open, and with fear in his eyes he shuffled back in his chair.

I must look as if I'm already dead.

"Are you afraid of me, Marshall Howe?" she said. "Are you afraid of the dead man who just spoke to you? Oh, yes, he's angry. You think you're safe because you won't die of plague, but you'll die of something, one day. You robbed the dead. You stole from their widows and orphans. Don't you think they'll all be waiting for you when you die?"

She staggered forward into the room.

"I've come for Mrs Unwin's candlesticks," she said, "and I've brought you a message from the dead, Marshall Howe. Because I'm nearly dead. Don't you take one look at these candlesticks again. Don't you touch anything of Mr Unwin's, anything. And you leave my little brother alone, too, and his dog! Or I promise you, you'll wish you had died of the plague!"

Her hand tightened on a candlestick and she held it like a dagger. "We're all trapped in this village with the plague. But you're trapped in your own wickedness, and that's a worse thing." With the candlesticks clutched against her bodice, she staggered to the door.

Candlesticks to go to the Unwins. I must take the candlesticks first. She stumbled back to the street again. Something in her head spun, faster, faster. She was spinning, or the world was spinning, her head was going to burst and spin away over the moors, and at last the pain and the tightness would go...

...Mrs Mompesson called her name.

CHAPTER

8

# The Smell of Herbs

The air was cool. The spinning had stopped. Something beautifully cold was on her forehead, and a breeze wafted over her. She opened her eyes and found she was looking at the beams of a ceiling.

She was home, lying on the floor. Someone was holding her hand. Lizzie. Joan was fanning her.

"I'll come no nearer." She could hear Mrs Mompesson's voice, and saw her standing just beyond the doorway. "I've been in a plague house today, so I won't come any nearer. But I can tell you from here, this is not plague. Have you had a headache today, Sarah? Do you feel sick?"

"Yes, Mrs Mompesson," said Sarah, weakly.

"It's too much sun," said Mrs Mompesson. "Out in the strong sunshine all yesterday and today, and without a bonnet, I think. Lizzie's been cooling your face with a cloth, that will help. Rest and be quiet, and have something to drink."

"Where's Robin?" said Sarah.

"Robin's here," said Lizzie. "And his dog. Can't you smell the pennyroyal?"

"I can't." Mrs Mompesson's voice seemed to come from far away, through a dream. "The air smells sweet today."

Sarah drifted in and out of dreams, all that day and night. In her dreams she took the road out of Eyam, but every road led back into the village. She dreamed about Robin and his dog. Good ratters. Good ratters, the Unwin dogs. The smell of fresh herbs.

The next day she slept late. When she woke, her headache was gone, and she found she could eat. Bread was good, freedom from pain was even better. Life was good, and today it was still hers. Lizzie came in, bringing milk.

"Lizzie," said Sarah, "You know about our dog and the Unwins' dog?"

"What about them?" said Lizzie.

"The Unwins' dog was a good ratter, and so's Penn," she said.

"Of course they are," said Lizzie. "That's what we keep them for. We've never had rats, and quite right too. Filthy dirty things, covered in fleas. Is that all, because I haven't got all day?"

"We've never had fleas, either," said Sarah. "Maybe the pennyroyal helped?"

*Black rats eating grain from sacks*

"That's why mother planted it," said Lizzie.

Sarah lay quietly, thinking hard. "Do you think that the plague could have something to do with rats?" she said at last. "Wouldn't it be strange, if it did? Because we haven't had plague and we don't have rats, because of Penn. And the Unwins only got plague when their dog died."

"What nonsense you talk!" said Lizzie. "Plague just spreads about in the air. Everybody knows that. You scared us half to death, you know, when Mrs Mompesson said you'd fainted in the street. We thought it was..."

"So did I," said Sarah.

CHAPTER

9

# The Burning

After summer, the deaths were fewer. They began to dare to hope. Then there were hardly any deaths. By the beginning of November, they hoped it was over. By the middle of November, they knew it was.

There was a great burning.

The vicar ordered the burning of anything that might still spread plague – clothes, coverings, anything that might be tainted. In the dark of the chill November night, Sarah held Robin's hand and watched. Livid flames roared their fury at the sky.

Mr Unwin had survived. He and Marshall Howe never spoke when they passed each other in the street. Andrew Merrill had come down from the hill and moved back into his old house.

Eyam folk could go out of the village, but they weren't always welcome. They were still the people from the plague village. Sarah and Lizzie went to Bakewell market at last, feeling as if it should be a day of celebration, with singing and dancing. It was a strangely ordinary market day. They moved from stall

to stall among people who had no idea what it was like to be trapped in a village, and never would know. Friends still stood at a little distance from them, with uncertain smiles. Sarah and Lizzie bought butter and cheese, chose lace and gloves, and went home.

Catherine Mompesson's Tomb.

*An illustration of Catherine Mompesson's tomb from 1859. If you look at the title page of this book, you will see a photo of the tomb as it stands today*

But Eyam had kept its promise. Almost four hundred of their friends, neighbours and families had died, but plague had not spread beyond the village. Every day, Sarah woke up knowing how good it was to be alive. She still checked herself for signs of plague, but not so often as before.

It would never be the same. There were too many empty houses. Too many new graves in the hills, and one in the churchyard. Only one plague victim had been buried in the churchyard, and that was Mrs Mompesson.

Robin pressed close to Sarah. "It's nearly winter, isn't it?" he said.

"Yes, love," she said.

He looked up hopefully. "We'll have a Christmas, won't we?" he said.

"Yes," she said, and smiled down at him. The plague couldn't kill Christmas, though Christmas wouldn't be the same this year. "And a New Year. And a spring."

For those who were left, there would be a future.

# Story Background

Eyam is a beautiful village, and if you go there now you can see the museum which tells you about Marshall Howe, the Mompessons, and other characters in the village. You can go to Cucklett Delph, the well (now called Mompesson's well) and the Boundary Stone, and you can see the cottages where plague first broke out – but you can't go inside, because they are still lived in!

*The Plague Cottages at Eyam*

In the churchyard, you can see the grave of Catherine Mompesson, and if you happen to be there on Plague Sunday – the last Sunday in August – there will be red flowers on it. Traditionally, the vicar's wife puts them there on the anniversary of Catherine's burial.

The plague was carried by the fleas living on black rats. The fleas then passed the plague to humans. Once caught, it could be spread by coughing and sneezing and by contact.

I made up Sarah and her family, but they are typical of families at the time. The Mompessons, Andrew Merrill, Marshall Howe and Mr Unwin really existed and the story about Mr Unwin and Marshall Howe is true, but I made up Mrs Unwin and her candlesticks!

# Index



# Glossary

**Bodice** part of a dress that is above the waist

**Boundary Stone** a stone that was used to mark the area limits between communities

**Jerkin** a close-fitting sleeveless jacket often made of leather

**Pennyroyal** a herb of the mint family with bluish-lilac or pink flowers

**Plague** a highly infectious disease that causes many deaths transmitted from rats to humans by fleas